A DORSET QUIZ BOOK

GW00644997

Testing your knowledge of town and country,
history and geography, yesterday and today

Jean Bellamy

Illustrated by Judith Fry

S.B. Publications

First published in 1995 by S.B. Publications
c/o 19 Grove Road, Seaford, East Sussex BN25 1TP

ISBN 1 85770 081 3

Typeset, printed and bound by
MFP Design & Print, Longford Trading Estate,
Thomas Street, Stretford, Manchester M32 0JT

Front cover: Where is this pub? Why is it famous?
Back cover: Name this church.
(Answers on p.64)

CONTENTS

INTRODUCTION

Here are questions for family gatherings, social occasions, or simply for your own amusement. If some may appear a little mind-bending, most will — hopefully — be of a less daunting nature than those posed on MASTERMIND! If you have to admit defeat and say 'Pass', at least you have only to turn to the end of the book for the answer.

So take your seat in the black chair and prepare to face the music! The questions may be taken at random if so wished; there is no grading system. Extra information has been included in a number of the answers to provide added interest, and it is hoped that by the time you reach the last page of this little book, your knowledge and appreciation of the delightful county of Dorset will have increased. As has mine in the compiling of it!

Jean E. Bellamy

1. DORSET BOOK OF RECORDS

One of the oldest and most distinctive of our English counties, Dorset's diversities are well worth seeking out. Here, for a start, are some Dorset records.

1. What is the highest point on the Dorset coast?

2. In which town church are the piers in the nave entirely of timber?

3. A Dorset church is one of only three in England dedicated to Basil the Great. Which is it?

4. Two Dorset hills reach over 900ft. Which is the highest?

5. Which is Dorset's highest-situated village?

6. This fortified house, still inhabited, is the only thatched castle in Dorset.

7. Where is Dorset's smallest pub?

8. This tithe-barn was originally the longest in Dorset.

9. Where is the only preserved Miz Maze in Dorset?

10. At the world-famous Abbotsbury Swannery, a white board at the top of a pole records an event in 1824. What does it record?

2. FAMOUS MEN

*Dorset had its fair
share of notable men.
Here is a selection.*

1. A memorial to this man who became an admiral stands 700ft above sea-level on Black Down.

2. Which six Dorset men were, in 1831, sentenced to be transported to Australia for seven years?

3. Brasses to the family of this man, whose ship fought under Nelson at Santa Cruz and the Nile, may be found in the church at Netherbury, where he was christened.

4. Where is there a fine bronze statue to William Barnes?

5. The ancestral home of the family of this famous philanthropist and reformer of the 19th century is in East Dorset.

6. The son of a well-known historical figure was christened in the village of Lillington, near Long Burton, on 1st November 1593. Who was he?

7. On whose memorial stone are the words, '*The Living. The Living. He shall praise Thee*', and where is the stone?

8. He was a lawyer on the side of the Parliamentarians in the Civil War. There is a monument to him in the church at Silton, Dorset's northernmost village.

9. He lived at Stalbridge, became the associate of leading scientists, and founded a school at Yetminster in 1691.

10. Who lived at Warmwell, was a master of a college at Cambridge, and on his death-bed foretold a great plague of London, streets on fire, and the Dome of St Paul's Cathedral toppling down?

3. THE ARTS

*'Craftsman's art and music's measure
For Thy pleasure
All combine.'*
*('Angel voices ever singing' —
The Rev. F. Pott 1861)*

1. A famous engraver was responsible for the windows of a Dorset church. Who was the engraver and which is the church?

2. People came from far and wide to receive tuition in copper-plate handwriting from this 18th-century handwriting artist. Who was he and where did he live?

3. This internationally renowned Dorset sculptress lived in a stable building in Woolland.

4. Another sculptress designed, in 1940, a picture consisting of cut-out figures of animals representing local characters, stitched by children of the village. It hangs in the church at East Chaldon.

5. This famous artist spent his honeymoon at Osmington, near Weymouth.

6. A 20th-century masterpiece of his is an effigy in a church in Wareham, and a statue in Dorchester is also his work.

7. He decorated internally the church of St Bartholomew, Sutton Waldron.

8. There is glass by these two men in several Dorset churches, including Sturminster Marshall and Sturminster Newton.

9. He was a Weymouth boy who became a notable artist and decorated the interior of the dome of St Paul's Cathedral.

10. This contemporary artist lives at Uploders.

4. CASTLES & OTHER DEFENCES

*'There is a castelet or pile not
far from the streate; and is
set on a high rokke hard by the
se cliffes a little above the
est ende of the chirch'.*
(From the 'Itinerary of John Leland')

1. This ruined castle, built by Edward I in 1280, stands stark on a conical hill.

2. Which ruined castle is alternatively named Bow and Arrow?

3. This hill fort, on the downs near Whitchurch Canonicorum, is the largest earthwork in the Marshwood Vale.

4. Little remains of this old castle situated in a park. It was built by Roger, Bishop of Salisbury, between 1107 and 1135.

5. King John visited this castle near Eggardon when he hunted in the forest. Today only mounds and trenches exist on top of a triangular promontory.

6. A triangular Iron Age fort stands $1^1/2$ miles up a hill, and commands glorious views along the coast and the Bride valley.

7. This site, said to be one of the most historic in the country, lies to the north-east on the county boundary, just past Woodyates.

8. This ancient Iron Age fort stands on the western spur of Bulbarrow.

9. Henry VIII built this castle on an island to protect a harbour entrance. In more recent times it was the home of a recluse.

10. In about AD 44, this imposing prehistoric hill fort in south Dorset was taken by a Roman army under Vespasian. It is said to be the finest in the country.

5. FAMOUS WOMEN

'An we've zome women not uncomely;
nor asheamed to show their feace'.
('In Praise of Dorset' — William Barnes)

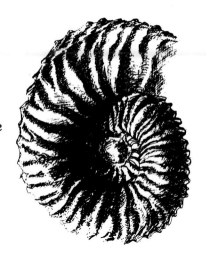

1. Who gallantly attempted the defence of a castle during the Civil War while her husband was away?

2. Which 12-year-old girl is famous for an interesting discovery she made while looking for fossils in the rocks?

3. Who saved her husband's manuscripts from being destroyed by a fire?

4. At which church, according to Hardy's famous novel, was Tess of the d'Urbervilles married to Angel Clare?

5. She was the daughter of Alfred the Great and her father founded an abbey for her.

6. She lived from 1795–1797 with her poet brother at Racedown House, one mile north of Bettiscombe.

7. Which Dorset beauty queen of modern times unveiled a fountain at Hinton Martel in 1965?

8. This lady, well-known in society circles in London in the 19th century, frequently visited the Sheridan family home at Frampton.

9. Who was the reprieved murderess who paved the mosaic chancel of a church at Portland?

10. There are two chapels in Dorset dedicated to this saint. They are both wishing chapels.

6. DORSET DIALECT

*The following are based on
'DORSET DIALECT DAYS'
by James Attwell.*

1. Who was the Dorset dialect poet who wrote: 'An' there vor me the apple tree Do lean down low in Linden Lea.'?

2. *'Po'me-zam!'* exclaimed the old man. What was he saying?

3. *'Zhe got the posh'*. Meaning what?

4. What flower was known as a *bithywin*?

5. What was the name of the farmer, author, and broadcaster who lived and died at Piddletrenthide and who gave the Dorset dialect to the world?

6. If you asked someone if he *'ould like a mar vur t'mar'*, what would you be offering him?

7. What was meant by a *mammet* or *mommet*?

8. If someone said 'It do need a cobweb!' to what would he or she be referring?

9. What would you be doing if you were *gooen 'ooden*?

10. What was meant by *hiling* a field?

7. MEN OF THE CLOTH

An un-named vicar of the time of James I,
wearing an M.A. gown and hose.

'The vicar here entombed lies;
Whose patron him doth eternize,
That his fair works of charity;
May not with him still buried be
But live in lasting memory.
(He died in 1614, aged 32.)

1. Where did a parson refuse to interrupt his sermon and thereby enabled Charles II to escape when fleeing after the battle of Worcester?

2. The Rev. John Audain, a military parson appointed to Charmouth church in 1783, is said to have fought a battle at Lyme Regis. With whom did he fight?

3. Which churchman holding high office retired to the village of Trent, lived at the rectory, and was buried in the churchyard?

4. A rector of Bradford Peverell, Dr. Howley, was appointed there in 1811. How did he later achieve fame?

5. In this north Dorset church is an effigy of 1625 to a former vicar and his brother, who was a doctor.

6. The incumbent of this church was the last to visit his parishioners on horseback. He also acted as village dentist, extractions taking place in what is now the rectory dining-room.

7. What fame did the Rev. William Crowe, rector of Stoke Abbott and son of a Winchester carpenter, achieve?

8. George Gould, vicar of East Fleet, built a church at his own expense. Why did he build it?

9. For what was the Rev. Christopher Pitt, inducted as rector of Pimperne in 1722, noted?

10. Two members of the Wesley family were rectors of this parish.

8. MISCELLANEOUS

*'ANY PERSON WILFULLY INJURING
ANY PART OF THIS COUNTY BRIDGE
WILL BE GUILTY OF FELONY AND
UPON CONVICTION LIABLE TO BE
? ? ? ?'*

1. What part of Dorset did Hardy call 'the Gibraltar of Wessex'?

2. What does the famous old bridge notice threaten to anyone damaging the bridge?

3. Near the group of villages known as the North Winterbornes is an iron signpost painted red. What is believed to. be the significance of it?

4. What is a Winterborne?

5. In 1939 a skull was discovered in this hamlet situated between the rivers Gussage and Tarrant. Which is the hamlet, and what was of particular interest about the discovery?

6. Which tower was built in the 18th century by Humphrey Sturt as an observatory or viewing point?

7. Why is Burning Cliff at Ringstead, Weymouth, so called?

8. This church stands in a field and is composed of five blocks of different centuries, expertly fitted together.

9. Which village has a telephone kiosk installed in 1942?

10. The village of Arne derives its name from the Saxon *'Aerne'*. What does this mean?

9. INDUSTRY

*'He loved birds and green places
and the wind on the heath. He saw
the brightness of the skirts of God.'*

(A memorial to a young man drowned
off the Purbeck ledges)

1. What does the lay-out of
   the town of Bridport tell
   us about its one-time
   prosperous industry?

2. What connection has the banqueting hall of Whitehall Palace with
   Dorset?

3. Where are there some quarries, no longer worked, but a popular
   tourist attraction?

4. A new industry started up in Maiden Newton some years ago.
   What was it?

5. The pottery manufactured in this Dorset town is world famous.

6. This house, at one time owned by The National Association for Mental
   Health, is now a prestigious centre of furniture-making.

7. This coastal village first struck oil in 1959.

8. In April 1914, a well-known chain store owner set in motion a
   plan to convert Hardy's Wessex into a model of agricultural
   proficiency. Who was he?

9. Cider-making has regularly taken place in Symondsbury since the
   1970s. Why?

10. What are Dorset Knobs and where can you buy them?

10. A QUESTION OF SPORT

From Corfe to sea at Ower Quay
Once marble proudly went
For banquet room and knightly tomb
And shrine's embeautiment.
(Bevan Whitney)

1. Every Shrove Tuesday a football is kicked through the streets of Corfe Castle to Swanage and back. By whom and why?

2. Which cruel sport took place in Marnhull, until it was stopped in 1763 due to damage caused to property?

3. Which village is noted for its Hunt which comprises one of the leading packs in the West Country?

4. A festival is held annually in Weymouth in April/May. What is it?

5. What notable Race took place at Weymouth during July 1994?

6. What sport took place at Blandford from the early 1600s, but collapsed with the coming of the South Western Railway to Salisbury twenty miles away in 1840?

7. In times past, this predominantly rural sport took place on large tracts of land in and near Cranborne Chase. It was followed by the gentry at some expense.

8. Usually supervised by a master, this sport took place at Wimborne Grammar School for over five centuries.

9. During this age-old custom held in Rogation Week, children were encouraged in competitive feats such as jumping ditches, climbing landmarks, and running along hedges.

10. In Sherborne in 1462 the Manorial Court forbade tennis and ball games. For what possible reason?

11. INVENTORS

*Necessity . . . the
mother of invention!*

1. What lethal weapon of the two Great Wars was made at Wyke Regis and tested in Portland Harbour?

2. Who in the year 1774 was the first person (known) to introduce the Cow Pox by experimenting from the cow on his wife and two sons?

3. The inventor of a devastating weapon of war lived in the village of Puncknowle. Who was he?

4. In the church at Tarrant Gunville is a tablet to a man who contributed to early experiments in photography. Who was he?

5. Which inventor carried out some of his earliest experiments in a hotel sitting-room at Sandbanks, Poole?

6. What experiments were carried out by Sir Alan Cobham's Flight Refuelling Company at Tarrant Rushton after the war?

7. A special china clay found in the vicinity of Tarrant Gunville could have been the reason for the residence for a time of a notable personality in a wing of the manor house there. Who was he?

8. For what was Robert Boyle of Stalbridge famous?

9. For what did Thomas Sydenham born in 1624 at Wynford Eagle, become famous?

10. During a cholera epidemic in the town of which he was vicar, he invented a sanitation system which became widely adopted. Who was he?

12. TOWNS

Stour's olden minster town, our own
Dear birthstead glides but slowly
through
Beneath its hoary bridge of stone
On both sides old, on one called new.
(William Barnes, 1800–1886)

1. Which town is the 'Port Bredy' of Thomas Hardy's novels?

2. In days gone by, this grassy area close to Poole town was a place — as its name suggests — to take a stroll.

3. For what feature — much photographed — is Shaftesbury particularly noted?

4. Which town has a two-tower minster with stonework of a curiously mottled appearance?

5. This town has an Abbey founded by King Ine for St Aldhelm in 705, and a school where King Alfred was educated.

6. Where did a king step into the water from his bathing-machine to the strains of the National Anthem?

7. Some of the approach roads to this pleasant market town contain avenues of elms planted by grateful Napoleonic prisoners.

8. This town in the Blackmoor Vale is noted for its 30-foot high Market Cross of yellow Ham stone, built in the 14th century.

9. A fine bridge with six pointed arches (c.1500), is a feature of this town on the Stour.

10. This interesting old town has earthen ramparts to the north, east and west, and a river on the south.

13. VILLAGES

'Homeward the countryman
  wends his way
In the gathering shades of night
With his dog at his side and with
  eager stride
And thoughts of a cottage bright'.
                    JEB.

1. In which village is there a pre-Conquest stone font with intertwined animals upside down?

2. Which village's name means *'A spring by the bare hill'*?

3. What is Tincleton's link with Thomas Hardy?

4. What is the name of the lost village which once existed under the shadow of Golden Cap?

5. Which village was a base for the first Airborne Division which played an important part in the invasion of Normandy in World War II?

6. Which village is famous for its maze, the survivor of three Dorset mazes of olden times?

7. For what feature is the village of Spetisbury particularly noted?

8. What does the plaque on a cottage in the centre of Broadwindsor commemorate?

9. This village has a wishing well, said to be the only authentic well in existence on the south coast.

10. What near-disaster took place at Powerstock, almost causing the death of the teacher's daughter?

14. FOLKLORE

*By the Runic Stone
they sat, where the grass sloped down . . .*
('By the Runic Stone' — Thomas Hardy)

1. Who is supposed to have leapt his horse over the church at Batcombe, knocking off one of the pinnacles?

2. One of these animals, considered to be unlucky in Dorset in days gone by, was reputed to haunt the road between Puncknowle and Swyre.

3. At this north Dorset village near the border, the chanting of plainsong, and the sound of a horn and the baying of hounds on Midsummer's night and Christmas Eve is said to have been heard by many.

4. What curious feature, to be seen on the heathland north of Studland, had local legend attached to it?

5. Where are there nine stones which are said to be uncountable?

6. It is recorded by a former rector that this village, the highest in Dorset, used to be inhabited by Gubbigamies that gibbered in the night.

7. What is the mysterious pillar near Batcombe, the Cross in Hand, believed to be?

8. At what time of day were the waters of wells such as St Wite's, Morecombelake, Symondsbury, and others having a similar reputation, considered to be most effective as a cure for sore eyes?

9. What is the legend connected with the village of Hermitage concerning an earthquake?

10. How are the villages of Shillingstone, Okeford Fitzpaine, and Child Okeford said to have got their names?

15. DES RES: A TOUR OF THE COUNTY'S GRANDER PROPERTIES

'Faire Houses, so full of Glasse, that one cannot tell where to become, to be out of the Sunne, or cold'.
(Sir Francis Bacon)

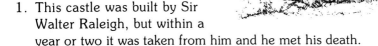

1. This castle was built by Sir Walter Raleigh, but within a year or two it was taken from him and he met his death.

2. This house, described as one of the most interesting in Dorset, was at one time owned by a family who, in Victorian times, were involved in a law-suit which went down in the Guinness Book of Records as the longest in history.

3. At which stately home in the Blackmore Vale, built c.1470, was a 16th century stone newel staircase removed because of a friendly spirit which rose from a nearby well?

4. This gracious Tudor Manor House built c.1500 had the distinction in recent times of being the 'most haunted house in Britain'.

5. Built in the reign of Henry VIII by Robert Morgan, this magnificent house has fine terraced gardens with stepped ponds filled by a stream.

6. Which stately home is the ancient medieval seat of the Trenchard family from Hordle in Hants?

7. This house, built by Sir Ralph Bankes in 1663-5, possesses a park with expansive lawns, and stands adjacent to a great avenue of beech trees two miles long.

8. The centre of this manor house in East Dorset is Elizabethan of 1585, the wings are Georgian and date from c.1740. The doorway of the porch is surmounted by a carved escutcheon of the Hussey family.

9. The Cistercians founded it in 1148, and 400 years ago it became a private house. Parts of it are today open to the public.

10. This house, now a popular hotel, dates back to 1603, and is believed to have been built by the Mohuns.

16. PUBS

*'Zmall glass o' ztout please,
dree bottles o' lemonade an'
dree bags o' chips
vur the nippers'.*
(From 'DORSET DIALECT DAYS'
by James Attwell)

1. Originally a blacksmith's forge, how — according to tradition — did the *Smith's Arms* at Godmanstone become a pub?

2. What connection does the *Nutshell Inn* at Bury St Edmunds have with the *Smith's Arms* at Godmanstone?

3. For what is the village of Halstock noted?

4. Which is Weymouth's oldest pub?

5. Where is the *Silent Woman Inn*?

6. Which village pub possesses a poem and a picture strip featuring a legend concerning a crab?

7. What is the name of the inn in Puddletown which is called after a Dorset cheese?

8. In which village will you find a pub called the *Brace of Pheasants*?

9. Where is *St Peter's Finger*?

10. This thatched pub was burnt down a few years ago and has since been rebuilt.

17. MISCELLANEOUS

The heath wore the appearance of an instalment of night which had taken its place before its astronomical hour was come.
(Thomas Hardy, 1840–1928)

1. A hill over 800ft high is covered by a prehistoric encampment. What is its name?

2. In the churchyard of this village near the north-east border is an old preaching cross and a stone mounting-block.

3. Where and what are the *Grey Mare and her Colts?*

4. What is the Dorset Cursus?

5. What and where are *Culpepper's Dish* and *Culpepper's Spoon?*

6. Where is the Quarter Jack to be found?

7. What are the terraced ridges to be seen on some Dorset hillsides?

8. This manor house, built in 1612 in Tudor style and designed by Sir John Strode of Parnham, was at one time the headquarters of the Ashendene Press. In 1950 it was acquired by the Ministry of Works for use by the Home Office as a Police Training College.

9. To whom was the Avalanche Church at Portland built as a memorial?

10. Beneath the gallery of which church are fire-buckets suspended?

18. ROYALTY

'. . . slain at eventide . . . and buried no worse deed has been done than this among Englishmen since they first sought Britain.'

(Anglo-Saxon Chronicle for March 18, 979 — from Arthur Mee's DORSET)

1. Which Saxon King was killed in the year 873 when fighting the Danes near Wimborne?

2. A plaque on Horton Heath marks the spot where a Duke was finally captured after a battle. Who was he?

3. Where was the material for the wedding dresses of the Queen and Princess Diana spun?

4. Where was a young King stabbed to death by his stepmother?

5. The building now known as the *Queen's Arms* is the oldest in Charmouth. Which Queen stayed there?

6. Where in Dorset is the only church in England named after Wolfrida?

7. A coffin lid in Tarrant Crawford church is said to be that of a Queen. Who was she?

8. Where did Charles II wait for, and miss his boat when being pursued?

9. What is Queen Elfrida said to have done to atone for the crime of killing her stepson?

10. Very unusually, two Kings are buried in this church.

19. WRITERS

*'Sweet and retired' was how she
described Charmouth as she
sat in unwearied contemplation
watching the tide flow in.*

1. Which Dorset author sits on a stone pedestal, his hat in his hand — and where?

2. A man who made a great name for himself as a surgeon wrote a book on Dorset. Who was he?

3. Which author lived (c.1735) at a manor house at East Stour on the site of the present farmhouse adjacent to the church?

4. Who was the most famous of all Dorset historians?

5. Frampton Court at Frampton, built in 1704, was enlarged in the 1800s by the son of which poet and playwright?

6. Which novelist lived at Chaldon Herring, and later at Newleaze Lodge, the cottage by the entrance to the churchyard at Mappowder.

7. Which well-known writer and broadcaster is buried in the churchyard at Powerstock?

8. This famous poet who came to Dorset at the age of 25 wrote a play called *'The Borderers'*, which was not published until 46 years later.

9. Which authoress wrote in one of her novels of *'A sweet retired bay, back'd by dark cliffs'*?

10. He often wrote in the vernacular, which he described as rich and expressive and free from artificiality.

20. UNNATURAL DEATHS

Brother and friend, if verse of mine
have power to make thy virtues
known,
Here let a monumental stone
stand, sacred as a shrine.
(William Wordsworth, 1770–1850)

1. How did Dr. Puckett, whose grave is in St Nicholas Churchyard, Broadwey, meet his death?

2. Who was killed while riding a motor-bike on a Moreton road?

3. 292 prisoners were sentenced to death by this notorious judge. Who was he?

4. Who was the young lieutenant who lost his life in the blowing up of the gate of Delhi on 11th October 1857? There is a memorial to him in the churchyard at Fontmell Magna.

5. Which famous poet's brother went down with his ship, 'Abergavenny' when, due to an error by the pilot, it sank off Portland Bill?

6. There are two flat, unnamed graves in Bincombe churchyard. To whom are they believed to belong?

7. A woman was murdered in Branksome Dene Chine, Poole, soon after the Second World War. What was her name?

8. Which naval lieutenant, who had taken part in 19 battles in the late 1700s, was killed at the age of 55, when fighting a duel at Charmouth against a former friend?

9. She was put to death at Maumbury Rings in 1705 for poisoning her husband.

10. The church at Folke is dedicated to St Lawrence. How did the saint meet his death?

21. ROGUES & ECCENTRICS

*'I see you have a lot of little barrels
in your boat . . . but I cannot allow you to
land them here. You must carry them on
further and land them somewhere else.
I have received strict orders not to allow
smuggling to be done along our coast
So be off with you!'*
(From 'Smuggling in Poole' by Bernard C. Short)

1. Which Sheriff of Dorset is said to have thrown open the doors of Dorchester prison to let out pickpockets, highwaymen, and sheep-stealers?

2. Who, in 1572, destroyed an entire village in order to obtain seclusion for himself near an Abbey?

3. How did William Watson of West Stour, an eccentric born over 250 years ago, make himself popular?

4. Lord Stourton of Owermoigne invited to supper at his house a father and son with whom he had had a lawsuit. For what purpose?

5. What was the nickname given to the leader (believed to be a local man of military standing) of the Chideock Gang in the 1800s?

6. Where is 'The Man in the Wall' tomb?

7. Which eccentric old squire always dressed in green, lived to be 100, never wore spectacles, and hunted until he was past 80?

8. Which notorious smuggler lived at Sixpenny Handley in the 18th century?

9. Another eccentric of West Stour was William Young. What befell him when acting as Chaplain to the Forces in Flanders?

10: Yet another notorious smuggler was Sam Hookey of Wick, Christchurch. How did he nearly meet his death as a child?

22. GOD'S CREATURES

When Julius Caesar landed here
I was then a little deer
When Julius Caesar reigned king
Round my neck he put his ring
Whoever shall me overtake
Save my life for Caesar's sake.

1. In 1888, the remains of an animal, thought to be 17ft tall, were found in an unusual geological formation in the chalk at Dewlish. What was it?

2. What creatures are represented on the pinnacles of the manor house at Toller Fratrum?

3. This animal was killed by Thomas de la Lynde, Bailiff of Blackmore Forest, at Kingstag, against the wishes of Henry III. What was it?

4. What animal may be seen on the downs east of Sutton Poyntz at Weymouth?

5. What animals may be seen at Edmondsham, near Verwood?

6. In which west Dorset village can you walk through the grounds of a magnificent Tudor house where there is a deer park?

7. An important fair used to be held in Blandford. What sort of animals were brought to it?

8. A bird surveys the landscape from the central gable of the manor house at Wynford Eagle. What does he represent?

9. Why is the village of Toller Porcorum so named?

10. There is an animal sanctuary in the Dorset Village of Church Knowle. What is its name?

23. CHURCHES

A country lane, a pealing bell,
A little church within a dell.
An open door, a hymn of praise,
A village choir their voices raise.
                    JEB.

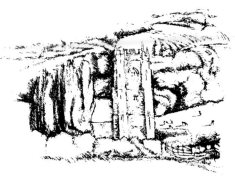

1. In which church will you find
   a carving in stone of a man
   with toothache and a man with
   a headache?

2. Six times a day the bells of the Minster of St Andrew, Yetminster, chime out a tune. Which tune do they chime?

3. This ruined church of Norman origin stands in the centre of a Neolithic henge monument and is said to be haunted.

4. This North Dorset Victorian church possesses a huge Norman-style central tower conspicuous from the main road.

5. A church in Dorset is dedicated to St Hypolite — one of only three churches in the county to be so dedicated. Which is it?

6. A village church contains a tall wooden font cover in the shape of a spire. It rises to a height of 20ft and almost touches the roof? Which is the church?

7. In Wyke Regis church is a room called 'the bones room'. Why is it so called?

8. At St Michael's church, Askerswell, may be seen what is believed to be one-half of an ancient sepulchral stone. Where is the other half to be found?

9. In the church at Stratton, north of Dorchester, is to be found a rare and remarkable staircase. What is unusual about it?

10. In which village church in mid-Dorset is there a clock dating from 1593 — one of the oldest in the country still working?

24. BATTLES

*'Never in the field of
human conflict was so
much owed by so many
to so few'.
(Winston Churchill, 1940)*

1. There are two bullet holes in the carved and canopied pulpit of Abbotsbury Church? How did they come to be there?

2. In 1142, Rufus Castle on Portland was taken from King Stephen by Robert, Earl of Gloucester. By what other name is it known?

3. This castle was twice besieged during the Civil War. The first attack was driven back, but during the second it was given away by treachery.

4. To what regiments did the soldiers encamped at Bincombe during the Napoleonic Wars mainly belong?

5. After the Battle of Worcester, Charles II fled to Trent disguised as a servant and took refuge in a manor house. What reward was offered for his capture, and what was the penalty for hiding him?

6. What occasioned the bullet holes in the ancient door of St Mary's Church, Maiden Newton?

7. This same church has bullet holes from a more recent date. What caused them?

8. At East Holme in the Purbecks is a bridge which is really two bridges — one old and of brick-and-flint, the other modern. What occurred here during the Civil War?

9. During excavations in 1857, what discovery was made at the earthworks known as Spetisbury Rings?

10. In this North Dorset town, Edmund Ironside overtook the fleeing Danes after the defeat of Canute.

25. MISCELLANEOUS

*'The swellin downs, wi' chalky tracks
a climmin up their zunny backs.'*
(William Barnes)

1. Where near Wimborne is there an
   ancient chapel built on the site of a
   former leper hospital?

2. How was a 5-year-old boy saved when, leaning over the parapet of
   the Abbey Church at Milton Abbas to pick a wild rose, he fell 60 feet
   to the ground? Who was he?

3. There was said to be a *'royal dog hospital'* at this manor house in the
   Blackmoor Vale, for *'keeping or lodging the King's sick or injured
   hounds at the King's cost when the Lord King hunted in Blakemore'*.

4. Which Sherborne clock-maker was responsible for the clocks in
   the churches at Long Burton and Yetminster?

5. An octagonal house was built in Nottington in 1830. For what
   purpose?

6. Swans fly over this narrow tidal lake, 8 miles long.

7. A curious double 'T' is spread around the 15th century tower of
   St Mary's Church, Charminster. What does it stand for?

8. A large house and park in this village lying south of Shaftesbury is
   now a public school. The house was built in 1877 by Alfred
   Waterhouse.

9. A chantry chapel dedicated to St Bartholomew was re-dedicated in
   1897 after becoming part of the farm buildings in 1552. It was
   used for many years as a carpenter's shop and to house horses and
   poultry.

10. In Trent church is an inscription over the archway of the Manor
    chapel which reads: *'All flesh is grass and the glory of it as the floure of
    the feilde'*. What is unusual about it?

26. COATS OF ARMS

*'In our halls is hung
armoury of the invincible knights of old;
We must be free or die, who speak the tongue
that Shakespeare spake'.*
(William Wordsworth)

1. What is the inscription to be seen under the Royal Arms of 1662 in Long Burton church?

2. This church tower was built in 1440 by Richard Duke of Gloucester and his wife Anna, and their Arms are to be seen on two shields on either side of the west door.

3. Over the door in the north front of this house are the Arms of the Bankes' family with the date 1663.

4. What inscription does Blandford town Coat of Arms bear?

5. What animals appear on the Arms of the Corporation of this same town?

6. Little Toller Farm at Toller Fratrum has a number of finials with heraldic symbols, including a shield bearing the Royal Arms. Which animal holds the shield?

7. Whose Arms appear on two shields on either side of the west door of Cranborne Church?

8. Amongst the Napier memorials in the church at Puncknowle was a helmet once carrying the Napier crest. What happened to it in 1975?

9. Outside the church at Tarrant Gunville, on the wall by the porch, is a Coat of Arms with three steeples and three Tudor roses. What is the inscription?

10. A Coat of Arms cut in stone in the porch of the church at Steeple, and repeated in scarlet paint on the roof, is the same as the Coat of Arms on a signet ring belonging to whom?

27. RAILWAYS

*The train passing under the
precipitous rock-face high above
Church Ope Cove, Portland.*
(The Eastern & Church Hope Railway Company)

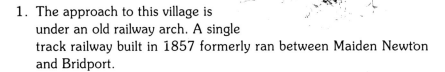

1. The approach to this village is
   under an old railway arch. A single
   track railway built in 1857 formerly ran between Maiden Newton
   and Bridport.

2. In 1975, when the railway between Maiden Newton and Bridport
   closed, this village station was sold and converted for private use.

3. The railway line runs close to this impressive village situated not
   more than a mile or two from the Somerset/Dorset border. It has an
   inn called the Railway Inn.

4. This village north-west of Blandford Forum lost two railways —
   one in 1965 axed by Beeching, the other a private line owned by
   a former High Sheriff of Dorset.

5. This railway has recently been re-opened, and you can enjoy a
   25-minute ride on a steam train to Harman's Cross.

6. During the 19th century, this village was given a halt at Holywell,
   about two miles to the north-east.

7. This Halt (now closed) was where one alighted to walk across the
   fields to visit a wishing well.

8. The railway line passed through this suburb of Poole in 1847,
   though the station was not opened until 1872. It was closed about
   100 years later, and a roundabout now exists where it passed under
   a bridge.

9. This village between Poole and Blandford had its own halt until the
   line was axed about 30 years ago. One of its pubs bears a reminder
   in the shape of a sign depicting a steam train.

10. A wall separates this railway from the road which runs parallel
    with it. It was built to prevent trains from frightening the horses.

28. MILLS & WATERMILLS

'There is a mill, an ancient one
Brown with rain, and dry with sun.
The miller's house is joined with it
And in July the swallows flit
To and fro, in and out, round
the windows all about'.
(THE WATER MILL from four poems
by Fredegond Shove)

1. In this village near Wimborne is an old mill, mentioned in the Domesday Book. Its wheel, in a glass case, is in the middle of a tea-room.

2. In the middle of Fontmell Magna is a converted mill adorned with a Venetian rotunda. What take place here from time to time?

3. Which industry, operating in the Old Mill, Maiden Newton, closed down in the 1970s?

4. This 17th century mill with 18th century additions stands on the banks of the Stour and is famous country-wide, even world-wide. Its history goes back at least 500 years and it was originally known as Neweton Castele Mill.

5. On the wall of this mill, also on the Stour, is an inscription of 1556, not easy to decipher. It begins: *'He that wyll have anythinge done, Let him com fryndly he shall be welcom;'* Which is the mill?

6. What is the name of the third mill in the vicinity?

7. There was a working mill here, at one time attached to an Abbey. It has connections with Angel Clare of Hardy's 'Tess', who worked here for a time to gain experience of the business.

8. Thomas Hardy's mill in *'The Trumpet Major'* was based upon this mill.

9. This derelict old mill of flint and stone buttressed with brick stands near the ruins of some old abbey buildings. It was once turned by the river Allen.

10. This mill on the outskirts of Wimborne is now a craft centre.

EAST DORSET
PICTURE QUIZ

This cottage has stood
through the following reigns

Henry VIII	George II
Mary I	George III
Elizabeth I	George IV
James I	William IV
Charles I	Queen Victoria
Cromwell Protectorate	Edward VII
Charles II	George V
James II	Edward VIII
William III	George VI
Queen Anne	Elizabeth II
George I	

1. This notice is situated on the wall of the Marigold tea-rooms. In which village?

2. Outside which ecclesiastical building is this three-faced sundial to be found?

3. This three-tiered, 15th-century preaching cross with its top missing stands near the main door of a church lying across a field. In which village?

4. This manor house stands adjacent to a church and occupies the site of a medieval monastic building. It passed by marriage to the Pitt family and thence to General Pitt-Rivers.

5. This spectacular church roof has almost life-size carvings of the twelve Apostles. In which church? *(Photograph by Judith Fry)*

6. To whom is this waymark a memorial and where is it to be found?

7. This Doric Portico, situated in Blandford Forum, dates from 1760, For what purpose was it built?

8. This fine 15th-century bridge over the Frome stands adjacent to a manor house which was the setting of a tragic episode in Hardy's 'Tess of the D'Urbevilles', Where is it?

9. Where is this Victorian letter-box to be found?

10. This Queen Anne house is a fine example of English Baroque architecture.

11. This Norman church has a central tower which was never finished.

12. A wing of this stately home was recently destroyed by fire.

13. What is this object, and in which church is it to be found?

WEST DORSET
PICTURE QUIZ

1. During the Second World War, the Bournemouth Art Gallery hung several of its pictures within this church for safe keeping. Where is it?

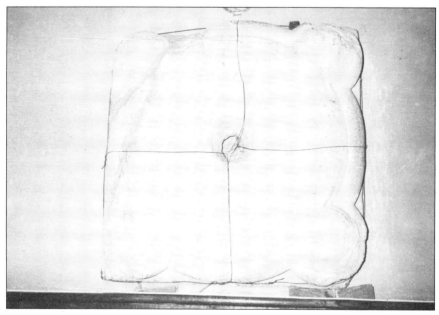

2. What is this object, and where is it to be found?

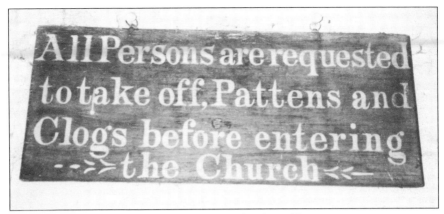

3. In which church is this old notice to be found?

4. This ancient cross on a 15th-century shaft is one of three to be found in this village.

5a. This church was built by convict labour.

5b. To which building is this the entrance?

6. This gateway once formed part of a Benedictine Abbey. In which village is it situated?

7. This shrine of Purbeck marble contains the bones of a saint. Where is it to be found and who is the saint?

8. What is this curious carving until recently incorporated into the outer wall of a church, but now re-sited in the chancel?

9. Outside which village church are these stocks to be found?

10. This well-preserved 14th-century Conduit, once part of a monastery, stands against a background of black-and-white timbered houses.

11. This ancient breakwater is said to have existed since Edward I's reign. Where is it and what is it called?

12. This font is decorated with circles and spirals. In which church is it to be found?

ANSWERS

1. DORSET BOOK OF RECORDS

1. Golden Cap, 617ft, so called because of its colour when the sun shines on it.
2. St James Church, Poole. The pillars are of pitch-pine from Newfoundland.
3. Toller Fratrum, a little 13th century restored building consisting of a chancel, nave, and bell-turret.
4. Pilsdon Pen in West Dorset and Bulbarrow in the Blackmore Vale. Pilsdon Pen is the highest at 909ft.
5. Ashmore, a hill-top village on the Dorset/Wiltshire border, standing 700ft high.
6. Woodsford Castle. It was built in 1337 and still has its arrow-slits and loopholes.
7. The Smith's Arms at Godmanstone, 4 miles north of Dorchester. It claimed also to be the smallest in England until that distinction went to the Nutshell, Bury St Edmunds.
8. The Great Barn at Abbotsbury, 272ft by 31ft, but now half-ruined. It was originally a grain-store, and more recently housed the locally-grown reeds used in thatching. It is now a craft centre.
9. At Leigh, south of Yetminster. It is 26 yards across and consists of a hexagonal ditch with a circular platform in the middle.
10. It records that on the 23rd November 1824 the high tide depth of water following the tidal wave was an incredible 22ft 8ins.

2. FAMOUS MEN

1. Sir Thomas Masterman Hardy, Nelson's Hardy — not to be confused with Thomas Hardy, the Dorset novelist.
2. The Tolpuddle Martyrs.
3. Sir Samuel Hood. Other members of the family had naval connections, one sailing with Captain Cook on his second journey round the world.
4. Outside St Peter's Church, Dorchester.
5. Sir Anthony Ashley Cooper, the Seventh Earl of Shaftesbury, of Wimborne, St Giles.
6. Walter, son of Sir Walter Raleigh. A copy of the entry in the Bishop's Transcripts hangs on the wall and reads, 'Walter, son of S.W. Rahley'.
7. Llewellyn Powys (1884–1939). On a hill between Chaldon Herring and the sea.
8. Sir Hugh Wyndham. Stripped of his office by Charles II, he was reinstated and made a judge.

9. Sir Robert Boyle. One of his most notable achievements was to show how air could be compressed, thus giving us the pneumatic tyre.

10. John Sadler, orientalist and prophet. He lived at the manor house.

3. THE ARTS

1. Lawrence Whistler. Moreton Church (1950).
2. John Willis who lived at Iwerne Minster.
3. Dame Elisabeth Frink.
4. Elizabeth Muntz whose tombstone, designed by herself before her death, may be seen in the churchyard at East Chaldon.
5. John Constable. He painted 'Osmington Village' and 'Weymouth Bay' here.
6. Eric Kennington.
7. The painter-decorator, Owen Jones.
8. Clayton and Bell.
9. Sir James Thornhill. He learnt the rudiments of art from another Dorset man, Thomas Highmore.
10. Sheila Sanford.

4. CASTLES AND OTHER DEFENCES

1. Corfe Castle in the Pubecks, a popular tourist attraction.
2. Rufus Castle, Portland, built — according to tradition — by William II.
3. Coney's Castle, where a battle took place between King Egbert and the Danes.
4. The old castle in the parish of Castleton at Sherborne. It was acquired by Sir Walter Raleigh who subsequently built the present Castle on a hill to the south.
5. Powerstock, originally a towering motte-and-bailey castle.
6. Abbotsbury Castle. Its walls extend for 300 yards.
7. Bokerley Dyke. Along with Grim's Ditch and Ackling Dyke, it formed a defensive line on the border.
8. Rawlsbury Rings. In 1951 a collection of sherds was excavated here.
9. The castle on Brownsea Island, built to defend Poole Harbour.
10. Maiden Castle, near Dorchester. It was occupied from Neolithic times.

5. FAMOUS WOMEN

1. Lady Bankes. She tried to defend Corfe Castle by pouring hot ashes over the enemy.
2. Mary Anning of Charmouth. She discovered an ichthyosaurus in the cliffs at Lyme Regis.
3. Mrs Hutchins (née Anne Stephens), when her husband, the Dorset historian, was rector of Wareham (1743–1773).
4. St Andrew at West Stafford. The village was called Talbothayes in his novels.
5. Ethelgiva (or Elgiva), for whom King Alfred founded Shaftesbury Abbey.
6. Dorothy Wordsworth.
7. Miss Ann Sidney.
8. Mrs Caroline Norton. She was a member of the Frampton family.
9. Constance Kent. The church dedicated to St Peter was built entirely by convict labour
10. St Catherine. The chapels are St Catherine's Chapel, Abbotsbury, and St Catherine's Chapel on St Aldhelm's Head in the Purbecks.

6. DORSET DIALECT

1. William Barnes.
2. 'Upon my soul!'
3. 'She has the money'.
4. Convolvulus.
5. Ralph Wightman.
6. A marrow for tomorrow.
7. An image, scarecrow, unsightly person.
8. A cut of any sort. A cobweb was a method of treatment with country folk which stopped bleeding.
9. You would be going wooding.
10. Standing the sheaves upright in stooks which were called hiles.

7. MEN OF THE CLOTH

1. At Charmouth. The parson was John Wesley's great-great-grandfather, Bartholomew Wesley.
2. An Irish chaise driver. He lost because he was delivering an eloquent sermon at the same time.
3. The ninety-ninth Archbishop of Canterbury, Lord Fisher of Lambeth, during the 1960s. He frequently conducted services there.
4. In 1828 he became Archbishop of Canterbury, and was one of the two men who broke the news to Princess Victoria that King William was dead. He later crowned her Queen.
5. St Mary's Church, Gillingham. Their surname was Jessop.
6. The rector of St Osmund's Church, Melbury Osmond, from 1855–1910.
7. He won a scholarship to Oxford and became public orator there. He is also remembered for his poem, 'Lewesdon Hill'.
8. The old parish church was washed away, except for its chancel, in the great storm of 1824.
9. He was a poet and translator of the Aeneid. Strangely, he was one of three rectors of this parish having the same name.
10. Winterborne Whitchurch. John Wesley (rector from 1658–1662), and his son, Samuel, father of John and Charles. Samuel was buried here.

8. MISCELLANEOUS

1. The Isle of Portland.
2. Transportation for life.
3. One explanation is that it has connections with Judge Jefferies and his Bloody Assize, and is the site of a gibbett; a second, that originally a barn existed here which housed prisoners overnight on their walk, in leg irons, from Poole to Dorchester prison. It was at this spot that the town crier would stand to announce the Court Leet to be held at nearby Anderson manor.
4. A stream that is dry except in winter.
5. The man's skull, discovered in the hamlet of Long Crichel, bore witness to an operation of about 4000 years ago to relieve pressure on the man's brain — today known as trepanning.
6. Horton Tower.
7. It is so called because in 1826 chemical changes in the rocks ignited the oil-rich clay.
8. St Mary, Holnest. In the 1960s it was saved from becoming a ruin by the efforts of its few parishioners and others.
9. Tyneham. It is cream concrete and has the familiar ornate roof, in the style of the times.
10. 'Aerne' means 'an abode or secret place'.

9. INDUSTRY

1. Its wide streets (for nets) with alleyways (rope walks) leading off are a reminder of its one-time flourishing fishing-net and rope industry. It grew its own flax and three flax mills still exist.
2. Portland stone was used to build it, after which this stone was extensively used in other famous London buildings.
3. Tilly Whim Caves, near Anvil Point, Swanage.
4. The manufacture of Porcorum sausages, now being sold extensively.
5. Poole, It is one of the town's most notable industries, and visitors to the showrooms on Poole Quay are numerous.
6. Parnham House at Beaminster, owned by John Makepeace and having recent royal connections.
7. Kimmeridge in the Purbecks. It was the first oil in the country to be commercially extracted.
8. Sir Ernest Debenham. The result was the 'Bladen Farm and Allied Business', a Central Dairy and model estate village opening up at Bryant's Puddle. It became redundant in 1929 on the opening of a central milk factory at Milborne St Andrew.
9. A cider-making press was left to the village that year.
10. Large crisp biscuits made at Moore's Dorset Biscuit factory at Morecombelake, near Chideock.

10. A QUESTION OF SPORT

1. By the Freeman of the Ancient Order of Purbeck Marblers, to maintain an ancient right-of-way to Swanage Harbour, from where Purbeck marble was once shipped.
2. Bull-baiting.
3. Cattistock.
4. International Beach Kite Festival on Weymouth Beach.
5. Cutty Sark Tall Ships Race.
6. Horse-racing.
7. Hawking. It took place on land known as Hawking Down.
8. Shrove Tuesday cock-fighting.
9. Perambulation (or Beating) of the Bounds, held for the purpose of reminding people where the parish boundaries lay. The custom was revived in Poole this century.
10. Possibly in the interests of law and order, because it was a textile centre.

11. INVENTORS

1. The Whitehead Torpedo, invented by Robert Whitehead (1813–1905).
2. Benjamin Jesty who, along with his wife, is buried in the churchyard at Worth Matravers.
3. Colonel Shrapnel (1761–1842).
4. Thomas Wedgwood. He was born in 1771 and died in 1805 at the age of 34.
5. Marconi, in a small sitting room at the Haven Hotel. From 1898 until 1913 it was used regularly as a wireless station.
6. Re-fuelling aircraft in mid-air.
7. Josiah Wedgwood.
8. A mathematician, he devoted his life to the spread of scientific learning, and improved the air-pump. By a series of novel experiments, he showed how air could be compressed, thus giving us the pneumatic tyre. In 1691 he founded a school at Yetminster.
9. Known as the 'Father of Medicine', he became one of London's leading physicians. He was the first to use tincture of opium, and introduced quinine as a cure for the plague.
10. The Rev. Henry Moule, vicar of Fordington St George, Dorchester, from 1829–1880.

12. TOWNS

1. The ancient town of Bridport.
2. The Ladies' Walking Field. It no longer exists, having been swallowed up in the new development scheme.
3. The steep, cobbled street known as Gold Hill, buttressed on one side, and with stepped houses on the other.
4. Wimborne Minster.
5. Sherborne, a town of yellow ochre stone with the atmosphere of a small cathedral city.
6. George III at Weymouth, which town he regularly visited.
7. Dorchester, the county town.
8. Stalbridge (once known as Staplebridge). On the pedestal of the Market Cross are carvings of Biblical figures.
9. Sturminster Newton.
10. Wareham in the Purbecks.

13. VILLAGES

1. Melbury Bubb. One explanation is that the sculpture was intended to show 'the overthrow of cruelty by the gospel of love'; or it could have been purely accidental.
2. Fontmell Magna. Its name derives from the Celtic 'Font' — a spring, and 'moel' — a bare hill.
3. In 'The Return of the Native' it is Stickleford where Diggory Ven, the Reddleman, came to live at one of its dairyhouses after his marriage to Thomasin Yeobright.
4. Stanton St Gabriel, reached by way of a narrow lane $1^1/_2$ miles beyond Chideock.
5. Tarrant Rushton, one of eight Tarrant villages along the length of the Tarrant stream.
6. Leigh. Now only a few green banks in a field, it was said to be of such cunning design that it took a man a long time to thread it!
7. Magnificent Crawford Bridge which crosses the Stour. It has nine arches and was built in the 15th century.
8. The night in 1651 that Charles II slept there on his flight to the coast after the battle of Worcester.
9. Upwey, near Weymouth. There are said to be few wells in existence clearer or fuller than this one. There is a café and gift shop adjoining.
10. Softening of the stone of the bathroom wall of a large Victorian/Gothic building used as the teacher's house, caused it to collapse. It no longer functioned as a residence and was sold in 1968.

14. FOLKLORE

1. Conjuror Minterne, a Squire of the 17th century.
2. A Black dog known as the 'Jumping Black Dog'. This strange belief was shared by certain other villages where sightings were reported.
3. Purse Caundle, with its lovely, many-gabled Elizabethan manor house.
4. The Agglestone, a sandstone boulder 17ft high and weighing about 400 tons. It is not known how it came to be there.
5. At the side of the road, just beyond Winterborne Abbas. They are thought to be the remains of an ancient British temple, and are said to be uncountable because the ninth is always out of sight.
6. Ashmore.
7. Some say it is a wishing stone, and some believe they can see the shape of a hand grasping a bowl at its top.
8. To obtain maximum relief, the water had to be taken early in the morning as soon as the sun's rays touched its surface.
9. A three-acre field was said to rise and be carried bodily over another field for approximately 300yds, where it came to rest blocking the road.

10. A baby was found abandoned, and the elders of the three adjacent villages met together to decide what each should contribute towards its support. Shillingstone gave a shilling; Okeford Fitzpaine (then known as Okeford Fifepenny) gave five pence; while Child Okeford undertook to rear the child.

15. DES RES

1. Sherborne Castle, in the ownership of the Digby family since 1617.
2. Upton House, near Poole, originally the home of the Tichborne family of Tichborne Trial fame. Upton Country Park has now been taken over by Poole Borough Council.
3. Purse Caundle Manor between Sherborne and Stalbridge.
4. Sandford Orcas Manor, the home of Sir Mervyn Medlycott. The 'ghosts' mysteriously disappeared on the expiration of that particular tenancy.
5. Mapperton House, near Beaminster.
6. Wolfeton House, near Dorchester.
7. Kingston Lacey House, near Wimborne. The avenue of trees extends along the main road to Badbury Rings.
8. Edmondsham House, north-east of Woodlands.
9. Forde Abbey on the Somerset/Dorset border.
10. The Moonfleet Hotel, formerly Fleet House, at Fleet.

16. PUBS

1. Charles II is said to have stopped at the forge to ask for a glass of porter. On being told by the blacksmith that he had no licence, the King immediately granted him one.
2. In 1982, the licensee of The Nutshell challenged the claim of The Smith's Arms to be the smallest pub in England. It was decided to settle the matter with a game of football which The Nutshell won, as they did the return match. The Nutshell is recorded in the Guinness Book of Records as the smallest pub.
3. Its inn, the Quiet Woman. She holds her head under her arm and according to tradition, represents a 7th century saint, St Juthware, whose brother cut off her head in a rage.
4. The Black Dog has the oldest structural remains.
5. At Coldharbour, on the heath north of Wareham. Unlike The Quiet Woman at Halstock, the Silent Woman does not carry her head under her arm.
6. The Anchor Inn, Shapwick. A fishmonger passing through to Bere Regis is said to have dropped a large crab. It struck terror into the hearts of the villagers who had never seen one before.
7. The Blue Vinny. The recipe for the cheese seems to have been lost during the last fifty years.
8. At Plush.

9. At Lytchett Minster, Poole. The name is a corruption of St Peter- ad-Vincula — St Peter in Chains — by which name it was once known.
10. The World's End Pub at Almer, — also the Red Lion, Winfrith.

17. MISCELLANEOUS

1. Eggardon Hill, consisting of some 20 acres enclosed by ramparts.
2. Compton Abbas, north of Fontmell Magna. Of the old church (rebuilt in 1867) only the ivy-covered tower remains.
3. Stones situated two miles south-east of the village of Long Bredy. They are the remains of a burial chamber.
4. A remarkable earthwork on Cranborne Chase, which may have been used for religious purposes, 3 $^{1}/_{2}$ miles long and composed of roughly parallel banks and ditches, parts can still be traced.
5. A geological phenomenon situated on the heath near Affpuddle. Culpepper's Dish, the largest of a series of conical hollows known as Swallow Holes, measures 100 yds in diameter and is 40ft deep.
6. High up on the west tower of Wimborne Minster. He dates from 1613 and started life as a monk; though since Napoleonic times he has been a brightly-painted grenadier. Four times every hour he carries out his routine of striking the quarter.
7. Strip Lynchets — the remains of an extensive Celtic cultivation system.
8. Chantmarle House on the outskirts of Frome St Quintin.
9. It was built in 1879 as a memorial to the crews and passengers of 'The Avalanche' and 'The Forest'. They lost their lives when the two ships were in collision in the Channel.
10. The church at Puddletown. The canvas fire-buckets, which were the property of the Sun Insurance Company of Bath, are dated 1805.

18. ROYALTY

1. King Ethelred (not the Unready), King of the West Saxons and brother of King Alfred. He was supposedly buried in Wimborne Minster.
2. The Duke of Monmouth, after his defeat at the battle of Sedgemoor. The Monmouth Ash which hid the Duke is now no longer visible.
3. At Worldwide Butterflies & Lullingstone Silk Farm, Compton House, near Sherborne, which originated in the early thirties at Lullingstone Castle, Kent.
4. At Corfe Castle. Queen Elfrida murdered her stepson, King Edward, in order to make her own son, Ethelred, king.
5. Catherine of Aragon after her arrival in England in 1501.
6. At Horton. She was the royal mother of St Edith, after whose birth she entered a nunnery.
7. Queen Joan, daughter of King John and wife of King Alexander of Scotland.
8. At Charmouth after his defeat at the Battle of Worcester.

9. She is said to have retired to a nunnery at Bere Regis.

10. Lady St Mary, Wareham. The Kings are Beortric (or Brihtric), King of Wessex, AD 802, and Edward, King of England, murdered at Corfe Castle in 979.

19. WRITERS

1. Thomas Hardy, near Dorchester County Library.

2. Sir Frederick Treves, the author of 'Highways and Byways of Dorset'.

3. Henry Fielding.

4. John Hutchins. He was born at Bradford Peverell in 1698, and was rector of Wareham from 1743–1773.

5. The dramatist, Sheridan.

6. Theodore Francis Powys. He and his two novelist brothers knew Chaldon Herring well. Theodore died at Mappowder in 1953 at the age of 77.

7. Kenneth Allsopp. He lived in the adjacent hamlet of West Milton, and from 1970 until his death in 1973 owned Milton Mill.

8. William Wordsworth. From 1795–7, he lived at Racedown Farm, two miles from Pilsdon, with his sister Dorothy.

9. Jane Austen in 'Persuasion', writing about Charmouth.

10. William Barnes. This well-known Dorset poet was also a schoolmaster and clergyman. At one time he kept a school in Dorchester, one of his pupils being Sir Frederick Treves.

20. UNNATURAL DEATHS

1. He was murdered by Jack Cox, a mental patient, when he went to visit him in his cottage at Sutton Poyntz.

2. T.E. Lawrence — Lawrence of Arabia — in 1935.

3. Judge Jeffreys after his infamous Assize following the Monmouth Rebellion.

4. Philip Salkeld, V.C. His father was rector of the church for 46 years.

5. William Wordsworth's brother, Captain John Wordsworth.

6. Two young German mercenaries shot during Napoleonic times for desertion.

7. Doreen Marshall. She was murdered by Neville Heath.

8. James Warden. He was killed by Norman Bond on 28th April 1792.

9. Mary Channing. This ancient site at Dorchester was the scene of 'Hanging Fairs' until 1767.

10. Instead of producing the church's treasures when asked, he gathered together a large number of the poor and needy. For this he was roasted on a grid.

21. ROGUES & ECCENTRICS

1. Sir Thomas More in the reign of Henry VIII.
2. Squire Joseph Damer, Earl of Dorchester. In its place he built, a short distance away, Milton Abbas, one of Dorset's show villages.
3. He was a quack doctor, and was popular with his patients because he charged them only 1/– a time.
4. Ostensibly to show that he had forgiven them. Instead he murdered them as they sat at his table. The surname of the murdered men was Hartgill.
5. The Colonel. The gang's smuggling activities were confined to the area between Seatown and Charmouth.
6. In Wimborne Minster. Ettricke, a Recorder of Poole, offended by the people of Wimborne, said he would neither be buried within the church, outside it, nor in the ground above it. He was granted permission to be buried in a niche in the wall, and was convinced he would die in 1691. He did not die until 1703, however, and the alteration can be clearly seen.
7. Henry Hastings, son of the Earl of Huntingdon. He lived at Woodlands and was buried at Horton in 1650.
8. Isaac Gulliver. He operated between Cranborne Chase and Poole Harbour. He was never caught and retired a wealthy man.
9. He absent-mindedly wandered over the enemy lines. Fortunately for him, the officer before whom he was brought sent him back!
10. By burrowing into the centre of a burial mound on Hengistbury Head. He was trapped by a fall of rock and permanently crippled.

22. GOD'S CREATURES

1. An elephant, thought to be of a species in existence one million years ago. Part of the remains are in Dorchester Museum, part in Salisbury.
2. A chained monkey holding a mirror, a winged griffin, and a lion with a shield bearing the royal arms.
3. A White Hart. This gave rise to a tax, levied on parishes in the Blackmore Vale, called White Hart Silver.
4. A White Horse carved in the grass, carrying George III away from Weymouth.
5. Horses at the Heavy Horse Centre.
6. Melbury House at Melbury Sampford.
7. Dorset Horn Sheep. They were brought from all over the country, and there is still a street known as Sheep Market Hill.
8. He is an eagle, and represents the 'Honour of the Eagle'. In Norman times, the manor formed part of a large estate owned by Gilbert de Aquila of Pevensey.
9. The name means 'Valley of the Pigs'. In the Middle Ages, the village was known as Swynestolre or Hogstolre, being noted for the large herds of swine kept in Powerstock Forest which in those days adjoined the village.
10. The Margaret Green Foundation Trust founded in 1965.

23. CHURCHES

1. Bere Regis. Similar carvings are to be seen at other churches, including Cerne Abbas.
2. The National Anthem.
3. Knowlton. The village has long since disappeared.
4. Christ Church, East Stour, rebuilt in 1842. Inside are two high galleries and a Norman font.
5. The church at Ryme Intrinseca.
6. Ss. Peter and Paul, Cattistock.
7. It is an ossuary, now used as a vestry. It derives its title from post-Reformation days when it was used as a depository for bones which came to the surface during the digging of graves in the churchyard.
8. In the church of St Candida, Whitchurch Canonicorum. The almost illegible inscription reads, 'Sir Thomas de Luda and Lady Alianore, his wife, lie here'. It is not known how they came to be sited in different churches.
9. Built around the 15th century, this narrow spiral staircase leading to the belfry is enclosed in a five-sided case with linenfold panels, all of oak. It is supported by a post ending in a sort of fan tracery.
10. Sydling St Nicholas. It is faceless, but strikes the hour.

24. BATTLES

1. They were the result of Cavaliers sniping at Roundheads from the church tower during the Civil War.
2. Bow and Arrow Castle.
3. Corfe Castle. Lady Bankes, her maids, servants, and a handful of men beat back the first attack.
4. Regiments of the German Legion.
5. There was a £1,000 reward on his head, and death for anyone concealing him.
6. Cromwell's men fired at the building when Royalists were hiding inside. The bullets themselves have disappeared in recent years.
7. A bullet fired from an aircraft in the Second World War penetrated a window.
8. Royalists held the crossing against Parliamentarian forces and overcame them.
9. The remains of a large number of skeletons lying side by side, believed to be Romans and Britains buried together after a battle.
10. Gillingham two miles from Somerset and two from Wiltshire — at Slaughter Gate.

25. MISCELLANEOUS

1. At Pamphill.
2. His stiff nankeen petticoats acted as a parachute and he was found at the bottom picking daisies. He was John Tregonwell who became High Sheriff of Dorset.
3. At Purse Caundle. It was said to be kept by John Aleyn who is thought to have lived at the manor or lodge in 1269 for this purpose.
4. Thomas Bartholomew.
5. To provide accommodation for those drinking the waters. Nottington was noted for its spa which was said to cure 'eruptive complaints, scrofula and loss of appetite'.
6. The Fleet, bounded on its seaward side by the Chesil Beach, and stretching from Portland to Abbotsbury.
7. Sir Thomas Trenchard of nearby Wolfeton Manor. It is a reminder that the tower was added by him in the 15th century.
8. The village is Iwerne Minster where Clayesmore School is situated.
9. The chapel at Corton Farm, off the Portesham/Upwey Road.
10. It is in looking-glass writing, its purpose apparently to remind the young ladies of the Manor of their vanity when they looked in the mirror instead of listening to the sermon!

26. COATS OF ARMS

1. 'Curse not the King, noe, not in thy thought'. Equally noteworthy is the quotation above it, 'Fear thou the Lord and the King and medelle not with them that are given to change (Pro. 24, 21)'
2. Cranborne Church.
3. Kingston Lacy.
4. 'Sigillam Burgentium de Blandfordium'.
5. Three lions.
6. A lion.
7. The arms of the Duke and Duchess of Gloucester who presented the tower in 1440.
8. It was stolen.
9. 'Hear lythe S.T.D. Parson — All Powre be but one. Earthe, Flesche, Worme and Bone MCCCCLXVII'.
10. George Washington. The owners of Steeple were the Lawrences, a family having connections with his ancestors.

27. RAILWAYS

1. Toller Porcorum. Until May 1975, a single coach with a diesel engine traversed the line, passing through this beautiful piece of Dorset countryside.
2. Powerstock. The railway was a lifeline to the village when the weather was severe.
3. Yetminster.
4. Shillingstone. The second line ran around the grounds of Shillingstone House.
5. Swanage railway. The station, with its reminders of bygone days is worth seeing.
6. Evershot. Holywell Tunnel was said to be one of the triumphs of the Great Western Railway. Some said it would never be completed as the sand kept falling in.
7. Upwey Wishing Well Halt.
8. Broadstone.
9. Spetisbury.
10. The railway across the causeway which separates Portland from the mainland.

28. WATERMILLS

1. Corfe Mullen.
2. Concerts.
3. Carpet-manufacture. The mill has arches over the stream.
4. Sturminster Newton Mill. It has recently been restored to full working order.
5. In the hamlet of Fiddleford off the Sherborne/Blandford road. The mill is no longer in use.
6. Cutt Mill, also no longer in use.
7. Bindon Abbey, near Wool.
8. Upwey Mill. Hardy sites it in the village of Sutton Poyntz, however.
9. The mill at Witchampton.
10. Walford Mill.

EAST DORSET PICTURE QUIZ

1. Spetisbury.
2. Wimborne Minster.
3. Cheselbourne.
4. The manor house at Hinton St Mary.
5. Bere Regis.
6. A member of the Powys family. It is situated on the cliffs near East Chaldon.
7. To commemorate the Great Fire of 1731 'and to prevent, by a timely supply of water the fatal consequences of fire hereafter'.
8. By Woolbridge Manor at Wool.
9. At South Walks, Dorchester.
10. Chettle House.
11. St Nicholas, Studland.
12. Athelhampton. It has since been repaired.
13. In Piddlehinton Church. It is an old turret clock.

WEST DORSET PICTURE QUIZ

1. Hermitage.
2. It is the base of a 12th century Purbeck marble font, and is affixed to the west wall of the south aisle of Yetminster Church.
3. In the porch of St Andrew's Church, Trent.
4. Leigh.
5. (a) St Peter's, Fortuneswell on Portland. (b) The Verne Prison on Portland.
6. At Abbotsbury.
7. In the church of St Wite and Holy Cross, Whitchurch Canonicorum. The saint is St Wite.
8. The Flying Angel at Winterborne Steepleton. Some consider it to be the Archangel Michael to whom the church is dedicated, others an angel cast out of Heaven. It dates from at least the 11th or 12th centuries and is believed to be pre-Conquest.
9. St Lawrence, Holwell.
10. At Sherborne. Here the monks used to wash and shave.
11. At Lyme Regis. It is called 'The Cobb'.
12. Hilfield Church.

Front Cover: Smith's Arms, Godmanstone. Dorset's smallest pub.
Back Cover: Corton Church, on the Upwey/Portesham Road.